READ ALOUD

HANUMAN TALES

Hanuman grabs the Sun

.............and other Stories

Author

VANEETA VAID

Nita Mehta
Publications
Enriching Young Minds

HANUMAN TALES

Hanuman grabs the Sun

.............and other Stories

Nita Mehta
Publications
Enriching Young Minds

READ ALOUD
HANUMAN TALES
Hanuman grabs the Sun
............and other Stories

Nita Mehta
Publications
Enriching Young Minds

Nita Mehta Publications

Corporate Office
3A/3, Asaf Ali Road, New Delhi 110 002
Phone: +91 11 2325 2948, 2325 0091
Telefax: +91 11 2325 0091
E-mail: nitamehta@nitamehta.com
Website: www.nitamehta.com

ISBN 978-81-7676-107-9

First Print 2013

Printed in India at Infinity Advertising Services (P) Ltd, New Delhi

Editorial and Marketing office
E-159, Greater Kailash II, New Delhi 110 048

Typesetting by National Information Technology Academy
3A/3, Asaf Ali Road, New Delhi 110 002

Distributed by :
NITA MEHTA BOOKS
3A/3, Asaf Ali Road, New Delhi - 02

Distribution Centre :
D16/1, Okhla Industrial Area, Phase-I,
New Delhi - 110020
Tel.: 26813199, 26813200
E-mail: nitamehta.mehta@gmail.com

Nita Mehta
Books
Distributors & Publishers

Contributing Writers:
Subhash Mehta
Tanya Mehta

Editorial & Proofreading:
Rajesh
Ramesh

Price: Rs. 145/-

CONTENTS

Introduction

Hanuman is one of the most popular Hindu Gods. He is also called the Monkey-God. He is the son of the celestial fairy Anjana and the God of wind, Lord Vayu. He is strong and intelligent. Hanuman also protects humans. Whenever we feel fear, we chant his name. In this book, we have taken the best stories related to Hanuman. These stories are written in simple language and accompanied by colourful illustrations.

HANUMAN GRABS THE SUN

Little Hanuman was taking a walk with his mother Anjana. It was a bright sunny day! Hanuman looked up at the sky and saw the shining, bright sun.

WHOOOOOOSH!

Mistaking it to be a fruit, Hanuman flew towards the sun.

Little Hanuman thought that the sun was a delicious fruit, you see!

SWAP! Little Hanuman grabbed the sun with his tiny hands.

"Yeow-let me go!" yelped the sun!

"This is not a fruit, it is a ball," little Hanuman squealed.

Bounce-bounce-bounce! Hanuman bounced the sun like a ball.

"Ow ow!" The sun cried in pain!

"Hanuman, let go of the sun. It has become dark down here!" Anjana said.

Yes it had! After all, we all know that the sun provides light to the whole world!

"Whee! This is so much of fun!" Hanuman continued to play with the sun.

"Let me go!" wailed the sun.

Indra, the God of thunder and lightening tried to stop Hanuman.

He bellowed, "Stop!"

But Hanuman did not let go of the Sun. This made Indra very angry indeed.

"Leave the Sun alone!" Indra boomed.

Oh dear, little Hanuman still refused to listen!

Indra picked up a lightening bolt from his bolt bag and hit little Hanuman with it!

"Whirrrlllllllllllllllllllllllllllllllllllllllllllllllllllll!" The bolt hit Hanuman.

Little Hanuman fainted and fell down, to the soft grassy ground.

"Aieeeeeeeeeee!" Anjana gathered her son and screamed, "Wake up Hanuman-wake up!"

But little Hanuman did not wake up.

Hearing her screams, Hanuman's father Lord Vayu or the wind god, arrived.

"Wake up Hanuman, wake up!" begged Lord Vayu too.

Little Hanuman did not wake up.

Lord Vayu was so angry that he shouted, "There will be no air in these worlds anymore!"

With a deep breath, he pulled away all the air from the atmosphere.

"Arrgh-choke-aaaaaaahhhhhh!" Nobody could breathe!

Lord Vayu was the God of air and wind after all!

Indra realized his fault and he quickly came to apologize to lord Vayu. "I am sorry I hurt your son. Please forgive me. I will bring Hanuman back to life," Indra bowed low in front of Hanuman's father.

Lord Vayu decided to forgive Indra.

Instantly, Hanuman opened his eyes and stood up.

Seeing him awake, everyone rejoiced!

HANUMAN AND VALI

Little Hanuman grew up to be a very strong young man. One day, when Hanuman was at Mount Rishyamukha he met a banished king called Sugriva.

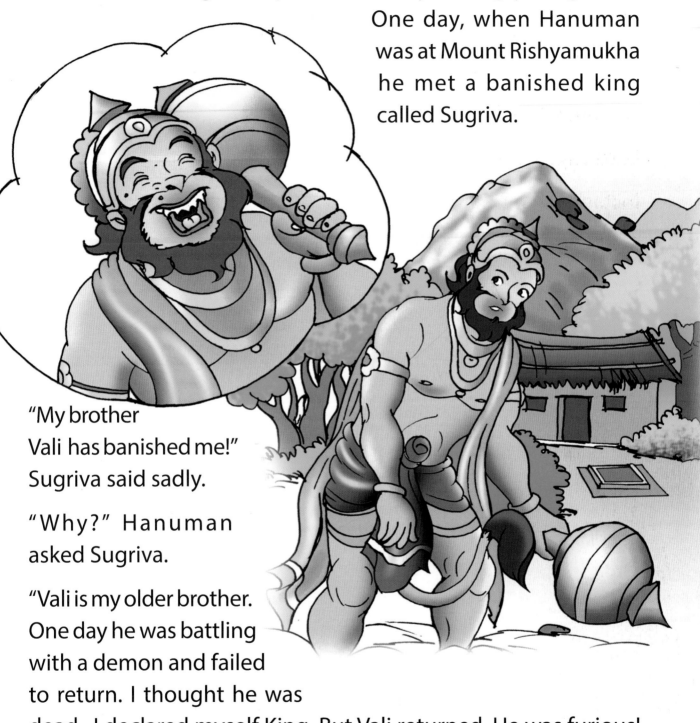

"My brother Vali has banished me!" Sugriva said sadly.

"Why?" Hanuman asked Sugriva.

"Vali is my older brother. One day he was battling with a demon and failed to return. I thought he was dead. I declared myself King. But Vali returned. He was furious! He chased me out of the kingdom. Ever since he has been very, very bad to me!" Sugriva wailed.

Just then a loud horrible sound rent the air. "AAARGHHHHHH!"

Hanuman and Sugriva looked up. A cruel looking, monster monkey hovered above them. The cruel monkey hit out at Sugriva. Poor Sugriva fell down!

"Oh no! that is Vali! Run!" Sugriva urged Hanuman.

Hanuman seemed not to hear Sugriva. He stared up at the sky. He observed Vali's flying legs curiously.

Hanuman stretched his hands and "glumpppp!" He grabbed Vali's flying legs!

"WOOOAAAAOOO!"Vali desperately tried to release his legs. But Hanuman's grip was strong.

"Let me go!"Vali screamed.

Vali hung mid air in the sky, unable to move away!

"Vali shouted, "What do you want?"

"Don't trouble Sugriva. Otherwise I will pluck you off the sky and kill you!"

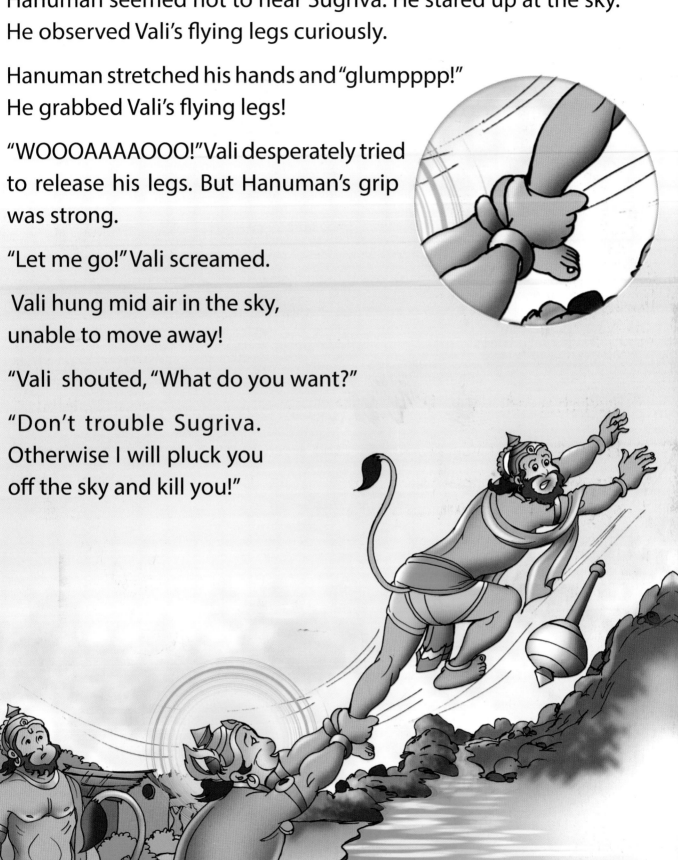

Vali was scared. He thought Hanuman was really strong! Hanuman could easily kill him!

"No don't do that! Let me go, I promise not to ever come back here!" Vali promised.

Hanuman let go of Vali.

Sugriva was very grateful to Hanuman.

HANUMAN LEAPS ACROSS THE GREAT BIG OCEAN

One day at the forest, Hanuman met Prince Ram, the prince of Ayodhya and his brother Laxman. They were looking for Prince Ram's wife, Sita. Sita had been kidnapped by the demon king Ravana. Ravana lived across the huge ocean! His kingdom was called Lanka.

"I will help you find your wife!" Hanuman assured Lord Ram.

An army was then gathered by Lord Ram with the help of Hanuman and the forest inmates. Lord Ram intended to cross the huge ocean to attack the demon King Ravan!

"To be able to do that we need someone to go to Lanka and find out how strong is our enemy," said Lord Ram.

"But the ocean is big. It is full of snakes and monster sea creatures. Who can cross this dangerous ocean?" Everyone buzzed amongst themselves.

"Hanuman can do this. He has magical powers!" said Jambuvan, the wise old bear.

BRUMMMMP Hanuman used magic powers to grow into a very, very huge giant monkey!

He took a huge leap and flew over the vast ocean!

The sea creatures peeped out from the surface of the water to curiously stare at Hanuman leaping across!

Hissssssssss!

Surasa, the mother of all snakes, reared her head too.

Now legend says that no creature could cross this ocean without entering Surasa's mouth. But that was dangerous. Surasa ate the poor travelers every time they stepped through her jaws!

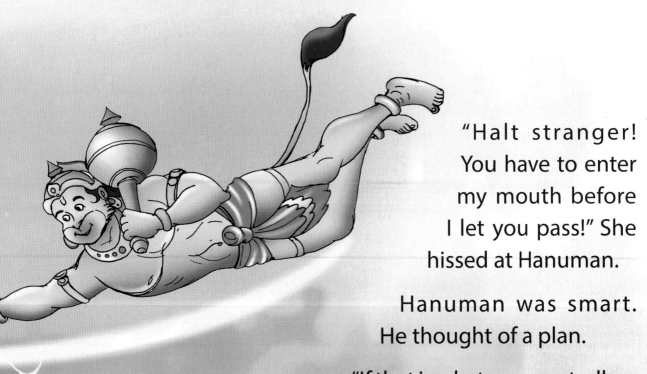

"Halt stranger! You have to enter my mouth before I let you pass!" She hissed at Hanuman.

Hanuman was smart. He thought of a plan.

"If that is what you want; allow me to step into your mouth Surasa," said Hanuman.

Surasa opened her mouth to let him enter.

Hanuman, with his magic, began to increase his size. He grew bigger and bigger. Surasa opened her mouth wider and wider.

Yawnnnnnnnnnnnnnnnnnnnnnnnnnnnnnnnnnnnnnnn

Surasa elongated her jaws wide!

As soon as her mouth was stretched to the maximum, Hanuman shrank himself to the size of a tiny mosquito and he entered her mouth!

When he hopped inside, he tapped his feet, and before Surasa could react to the tiny irritant on her tongue, he hopped out!

"Surasa, I have fulfilled the condition of entering your mouth. Now allow me to go further!" Hanuman boomed.

Surasa realized how she had been tricked.

"Um-whoooom, um!" She gulped and shrank her mouth back to normal.

"You are very clever Hanuman. For your smartness, you may cross the ocean!" Surasa moved aside to give Hanuman a pass. Hanuman flew towards Lanka.

THE BURNING OF LANKA

Hanuman had secretly arrived in Lanka and met Sita. He was able to give her a message from Ram, her husband.

Ravan heard of this and a hunt to capture Hanuman began!
Oh dear, Hanuman was caught and brought before Ravan.

When Hanuman arrived at the court, he was humiliated by Ravan and his courtiers. Hanuman really did not care. He promptly let his tail grow by the magic he had.

He made himself a tower with his tail. He sat atop the 'tail tower'. "I sit higher than you Ravan!" Hanuman told the furious Ravan.

29

Ravan began to call Ram names. Oh dear, Hanuman would have none of that!

Hanuman slapped Ravan so hard that his crowns fell off!

Ravan was so angry that he ordered that Hanuman's tail to be set on fire!

Swhooooooosh! Hanuman's tail was set afire!

Hanuman was not at all annoyed. He just leapt up into the air and ran out of the palace. Waving his tail, Hanuman leapt from roof top to roof top setting the mansions and palaces on fire. Soon, the whole city was in flames.

"Arrrrrrerrrgh!" Ravan watched helplessly. But he could not do anything. All this was Ravan's fault. After all it was really stupid of him to treat Hanuman like that, don't you agree?

THE BRIDGE TO LANKA

"How do we cross over to Lanka with our army?" Ram questioned again and again, to Hanuman and Laxman. You see Lanka was very far away and the rest of them did not have magical power like Hanuman to fly over the ocean.

'The ocean separating us from Lanka is too big. Everything sinks into its waters… hmmmm… how do we cross over to Lanka?!' Ram was thinking when suddenly,

WHOOOOOOOSH!

The Sea God Varuna rose from the waters and said, "Do not worry Ram. Throw stones into my surface. I will make sure no stone sinks. Make a floating stone bridge and cross over!"

Everyone clapped hearing this solution.

Soon Ram's army began to built the 'stone bridge'. Hanuman wrote Lord Ram's name on each stone and who threw in to the waters. The bridge was quickly completed. "Hurrrah!" everyone rejoiced.

One by one, in one long trail, Ram's army began to cross.

"Yaaaaarghhhhhh!" Ravan yelled angrily when he saw the army crossing over. With one powerful move, he threw damaging magic missiles at the bridge.

Oh no! Just as the army was going to step on to the shores of Lanka, Ravan's missiles destroyed the last leg of the bridge creating a huge gap. "How do we cross now?" the confused soldiers wondered looking at the huge gap between the bridge and shore.

Zooooom! Hanuman arrived. He knew what he had to do. With his magic, he began to grow. Whooooooooooooooooooooooom! He grew to many folds his size!

Then you know what he did?

He stretched and lay over the gap! Hanuman he bridged the gap with his body.

Ram and his army easily crossed over Hanuman's body and reached the shore.

HANUMAN CARRIES A MOUNTAIN!

Laxman, Lord Ram's brother was badly injured in the war against Ravan. Lord Ram was very worried. Hanuman felt sorry for him.

"What can I do to help?"

"The best doctor in of these parts lives in Lanka. His name is Sushena. Fetch Sushena!"

Hanuman immediately flew to Lanka.

Once he reached the doctor's hut, Hanuman lifted the hut and carried it back to the forest!

When they returned to the forest, the doctor rushed to Laxman.

"Laxman can be cured by a special, medicinal plant called "*Sanjeevani buti*". This plant grows on a hill in the Himalayan range of mountains. "said the doctor."

Hanuman readily decided to fly to the mountain to get the special plant!

"Wait Hanuman." stopped the doctor. "Hanuman, this plant has to be brought to me before the setting of the moon or the rising of the sun!"

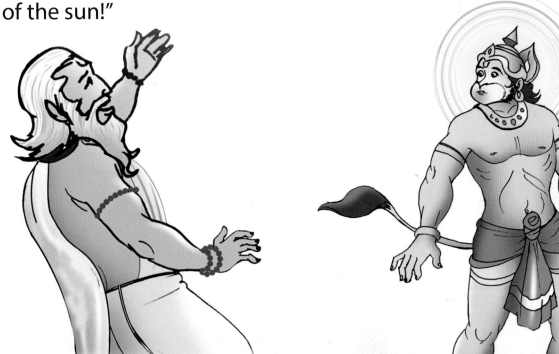

Hanuman plucked the moon from the sky and roused the sun from its sleep. We all know the sun sleeps when the moon is up don't we? He settled the sun and moon under each of his arms! Then he flew on! Now why would Hanuman do that?

Because he did not want a setting moon or rising sun to interfere with his task!

"Let go!" reproached the Moon.

"Yawn l-et go!" sleepily said the sun.

Hanuman reached the mountain.

Hanuman was confused. To him all the plants on the mountain peak looked the same!

'Now which one is the *Sanjeevani buti?*' wondered Hanuman.

'I have an idea!' Hanuman exclaimed.

You know what his idea was?

He decided to pick up the huge big mountain and carry it to the doctor!

Returning with the mountain, Hanuman called the doctor, "Please pick out the plant yourself! I have brought the mountain to you!"

The doctor quickly identified the plant. The doctor began to make the medicine.

He completed making the medicine. Then he fed the medicine to Laxman. As soon as Laxman had the medicine, he opened his eyes. *He was cured!*

Lord Ram hugged his brother.

Hanuman quickly released the sun and the moon.

Everyone clapped. They thought Hanuman was indeed very clever!

Activity

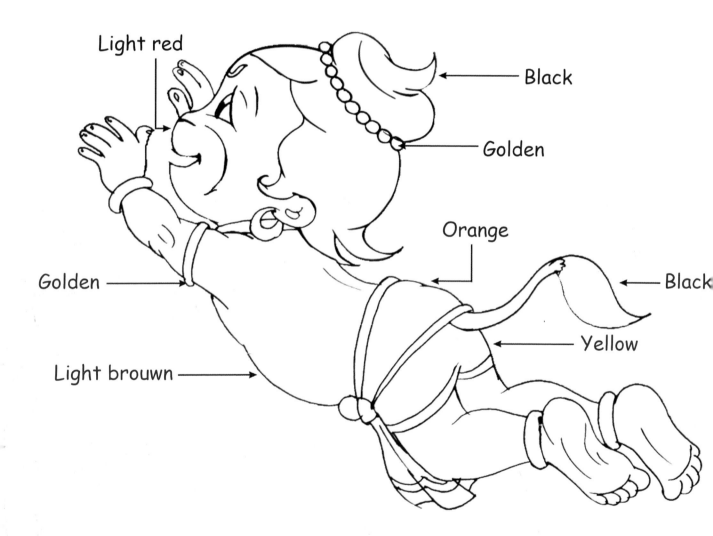

Light red

Black

Golden

Orange

Black

Golden

Yellow

Light brouwn

ODD ONE OUT
WHO WAS NOT IN THE STORY?

MATCH THE SHADOW

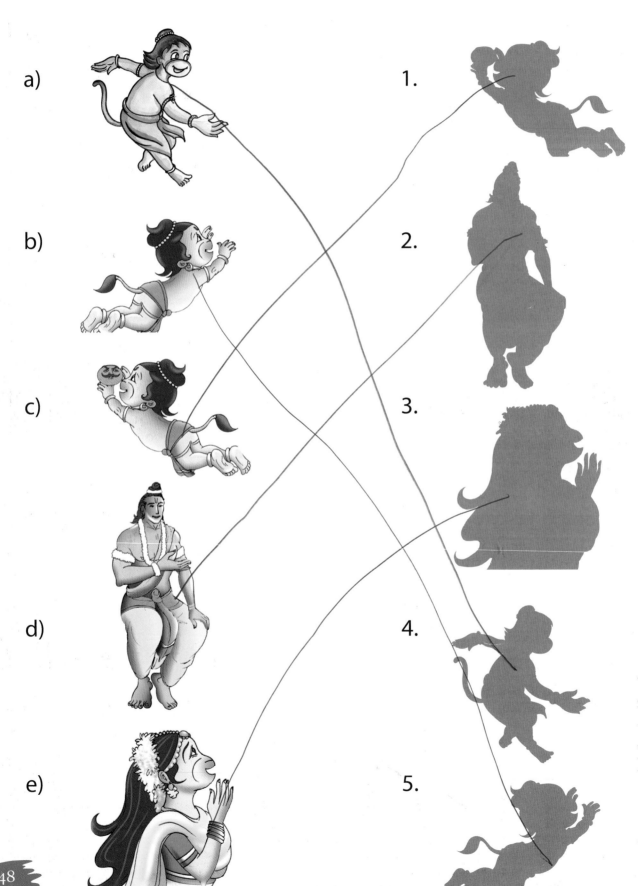

Answers: a4, b5, c1, d2, e3